# Hi, MuM! Hi, DaD!

# Hi, Mum!
# Hi, Dad!

101 Cartoons for
New Parents
by Lynn Johnston

**OWL PRESS**

Published by Owl Press, P.O. Box 315 Downton, Salisbury,
Wiltshire. SP5 3YE. July 1993
Printed in the UK by BPCC Wheatons Ltd, Exeter.

British Library Cataloguing - in - Publication Data. A catalogue
record for this book is available from the British Library.

Publisher's ISBN: 0 9515917 7 0

# The First Year of Life

A tiny bundle of life is placed in your arms, and at first it's hard to believe that you are now a parent. The overwhelming feeling of responsibility for another life, the pride and joy in your "creation", but also feelings of inadequacy in your new role frequently surface during that first year.

Lynn Johnston, with humour and sensitivity, creates cartoons that depict the feelings and reactions of parents as they learn to respond to the needs of the growing child, to the reactions of the in-laws and relatives, to the pressures of the mass media, the experts and the child-rearing fads. As we laugh at the captions we are reminded of the incredible amount of hardship experienced by parents during the baby's first year - the loss of sleep, the feeling of helplessness when the baby acquires new skills, as he or she learns to reach and grasp objects, sit up, crawl and finally becomes upright and mobile.

The baby becomes a "real" personality and enriches the life of the family. The joy experienced by the parents makes the struggle well worthwhile. The recognition of this joy is captured in the last cartoon: "To think that before we had a baby, this was just the same old park!"

With a few deft strokes of her pen, Lynn Johnston shows us what the first year of life is like. Her delightfully subtle cartoons at once make the hardships of life with baby more bearable.

MARY BLUM, PSYCHOLOGIST

7

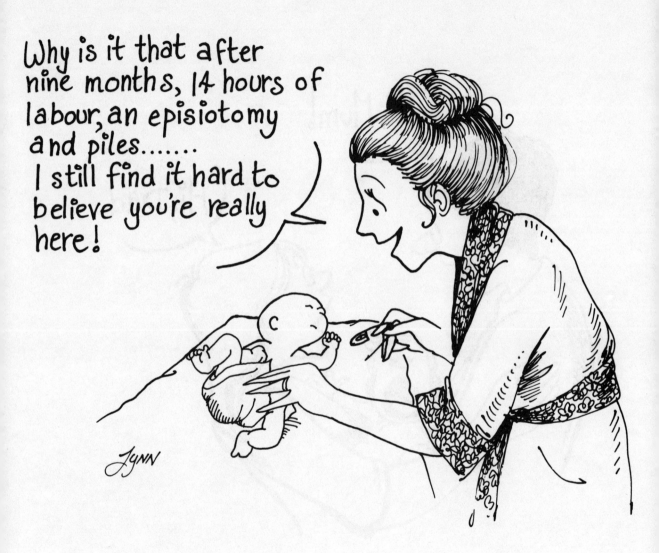

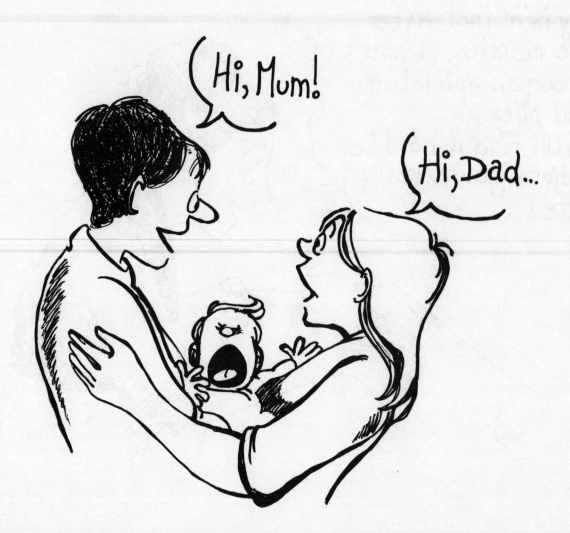

11

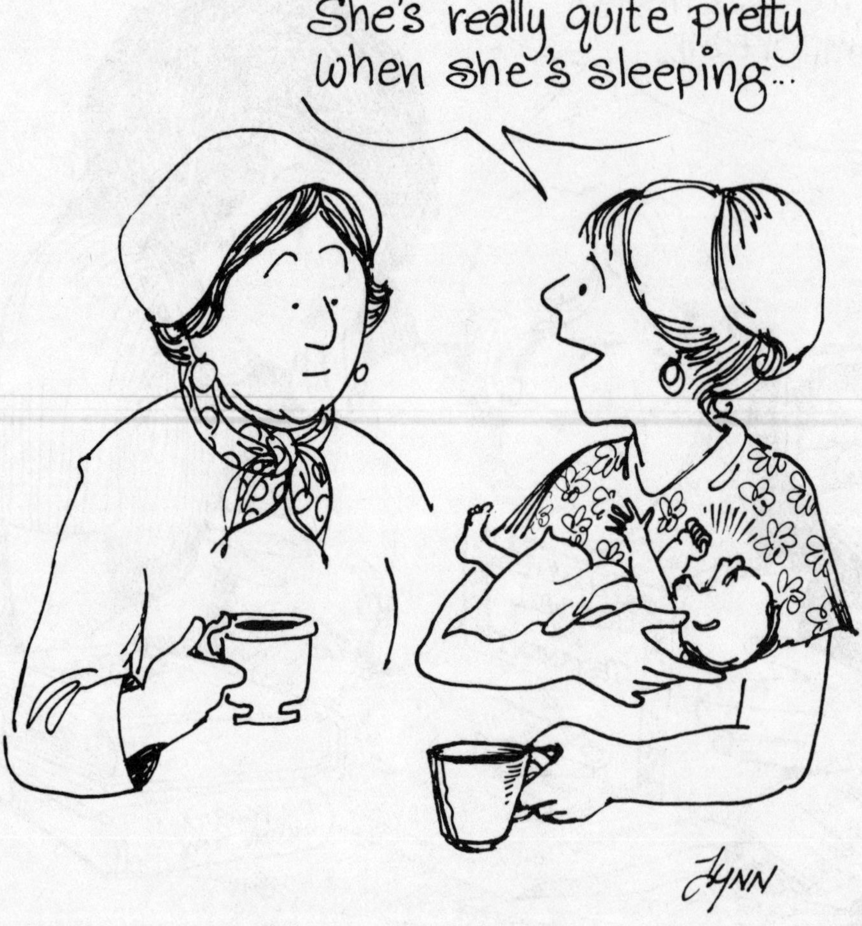
She's really quite pretty when she's sleeping...
LYNN

13

14

15

18

19

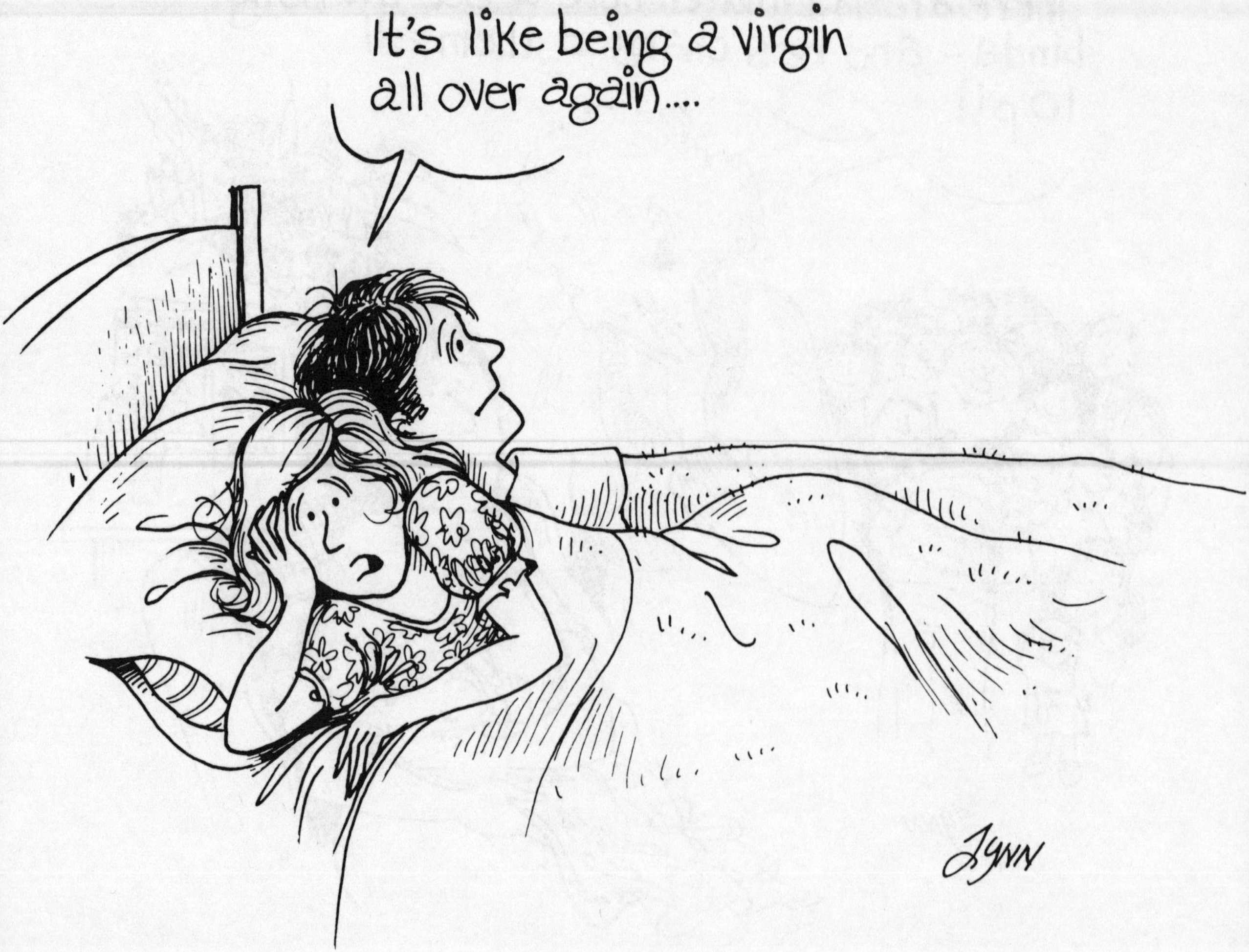
It's like being a virgin all over again....
LYNN

23

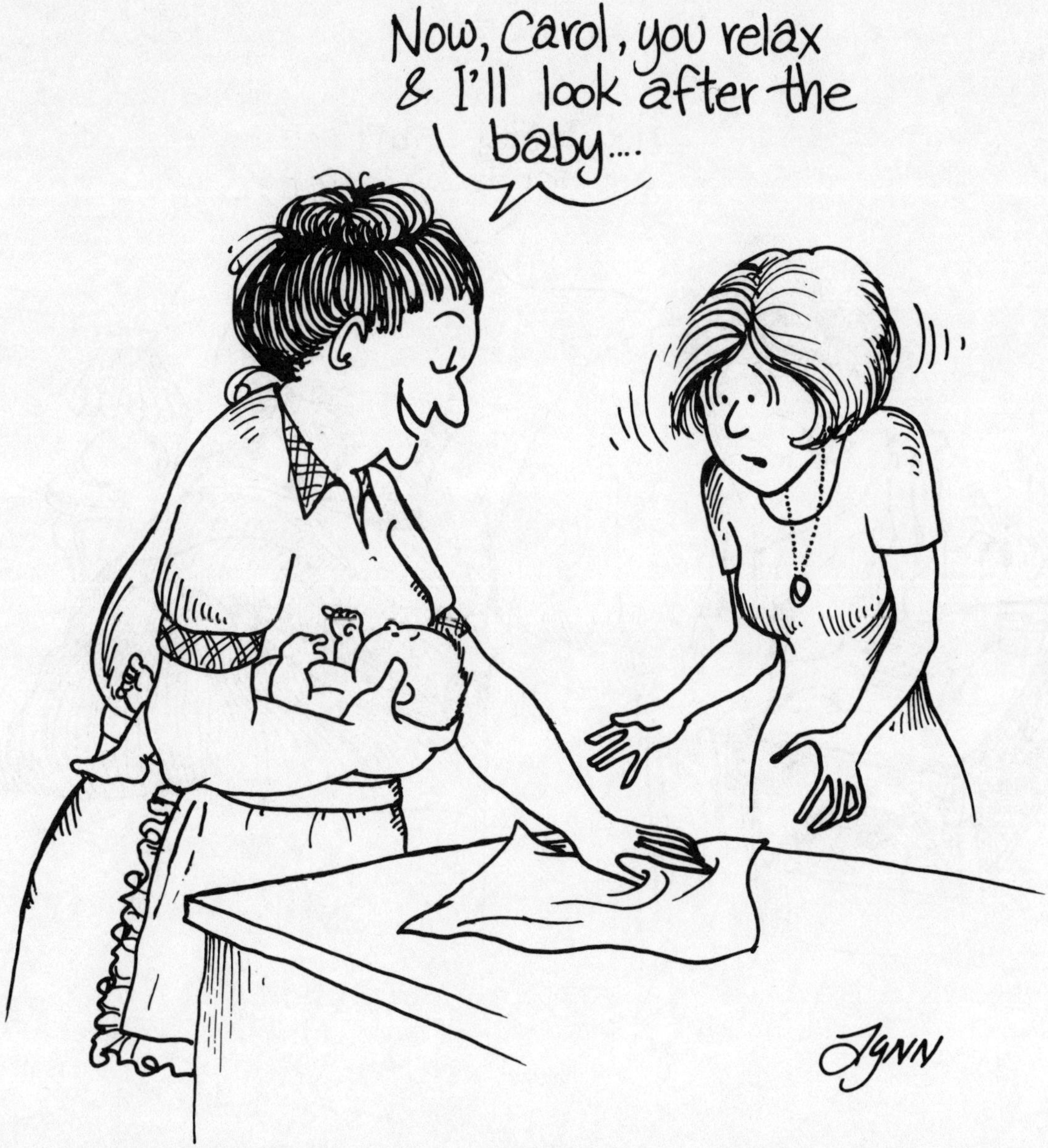
Now, Carol, you relax & I'll look after the baby....
LYNN

Hey, Dad, where's this soft spot everyone's talking about?
SUNDAY
LYNN

29

Half the battle is not letting _them_ know that you don't know what the heck you're doing!

37

I've tried feeding and rocking...and singing...and burping and bathing and pleading...and walking and shouting and whispering and... changing... and....

Dear Mom, you ask if we enjoy parenthood. Well, after 3 weeks of getting used to the situation, I can safely say ~~that we are already~~ that ~~things are~~ ~~that the baby is~~ Mom, can you make it out here?

Lynn

45

48

49

51

57

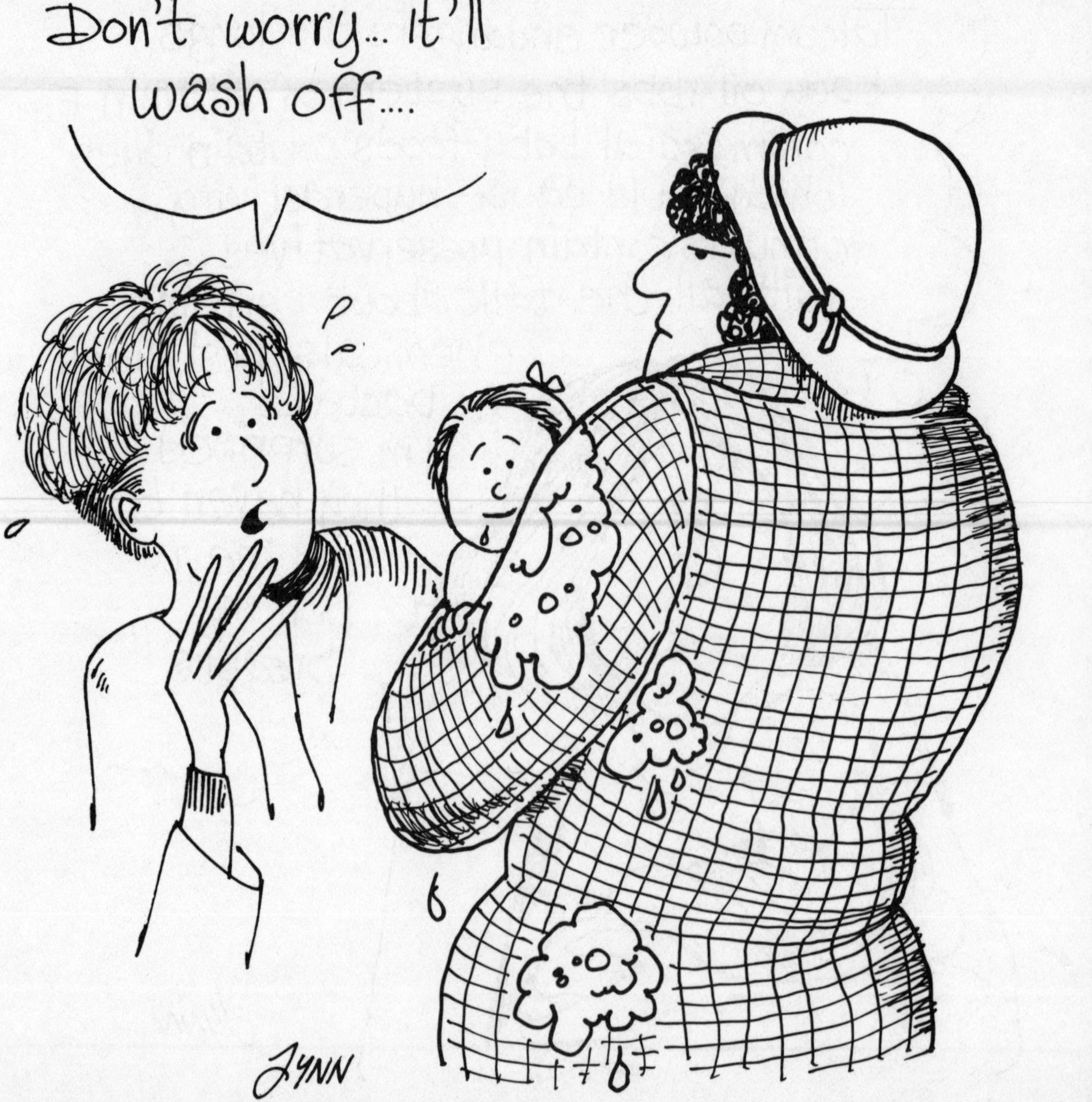
Don't worry... it'll wash off....
LYNN

I know what you're going through Danny. When my little sister was born, I lost all interest in sports & science — took up squeaky toys talked gibberish, & demanded late night feeds.

Wow! If finding his fingers makes him THIS happy-wait'll he discovers ORIFICES!!
LYNN

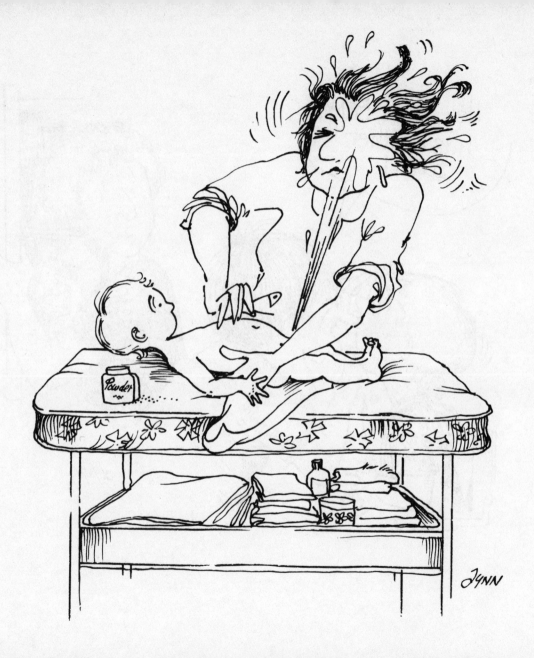

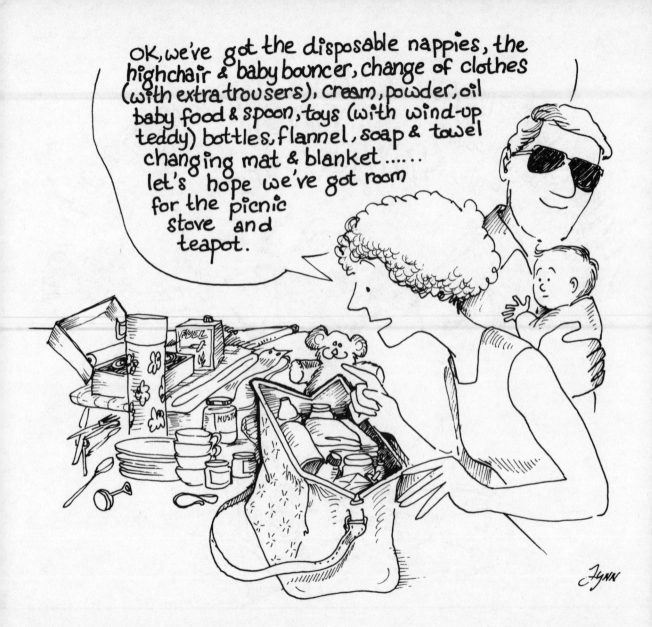

# Meet Lynn Johnston

Lynn Johnston is the world's top female cartoonist.
She draws much of her material from close
observation of her family. Lynn's deft, humorous
depictions of life with children have provided her
with material for three books published in the
United Kingdom by Owl Press.

# & Her Books:

## DAVID, WE'RE PREGNANT!

101 laughing-out-loud cartoons on
the humorous side of conceiving
and giving birth. A great present,
it's the perfect way to bolster the
spirits of any expectant couple.

ISBN 0 9515917 6 2

## HI, MUM! HI, DAD!

A side-splitting sequel to DAVID,
WE'RE PREGNANT! 101 cartoons
on the first year of childrearing -
all those late nights, early morning
wakings and other traumatic
"emergencies".

ISBN 0 9515917 7 0

## DO THEY EVER GROW UP?

This third in her series of cartoon
books is a hilarious survival guide
for parents of the tantrum and
dummy brigade, as well as a
hilarious memory book for parents
who have lived through it.

ISBN 0 9515917 8 9